SECTION 427

ROW 20

SEAT 17

SUPER BOWL LIV

THE NIGHT THE KINGDOM ROSE AGAIN

FEBRUARY 2, 2020 MIAMI, FL

Written by Jason Sivewright

Illustrations by Kevin & Kristen Howdeshell

So much can pass in fifty years.

A cowardly lion can brave his fears.

The world can turn to Royal Blue.

Some dreams stay dreams while some come true.

One dream that hadn't come to pass
Though cloaked in KC pride and class.
Our Chiefs for whom we cheer and chop
Had failed to reach the mountain's top.

LOUD AND PROUD!

The Super Bowl! The game of games!

Where football's finest make their names.

Each time the summit seemed in view

Our Chiefs would lose by just a few.

"What's going on?" the fans would ask.

"It's OUR coach with the best mustache!"

From underneath that furry lip

Came plays that made defenders trip...

And slip and stumble all around.

But right before they'd hit the ground

The other team would find its feet

And leave the Chiefs to taste defeat.

Then up from Tyler, Texas came
A young gunslinger by the name
Of Pat Mahomes to be exact.
Now HE was KC's quarterback.

He flicked the pigskin like horseshoes

And rocked a mop of curly-cues.

With style and grace he took the helm

And left defenders overwhelmed.

A no-look pass, a bomb, a fade
This dude made throws that no one made!

Touchdown Kelce!

Touchdown Hill!

Our Chiefs began to win at will!

With Mahomes' arm and Coach Reid's mind
It seemed that this was KC's time!
Then, in their way stepped Brady's Pats
As pesky as a swarm of gnats.

Our war with them went back and forth
But left the Chiefs one touchdown short.
Our boys in red chose not to mope.
The road ahead was paved with hope.

As if our Chiefs needed more swagger
They went and got The Honey Badger.
So all opponents best beware...
THE HONEY BADGER DOESN'T CARE!

Four straight wins to start the season
But, then, for a long list of reasons
Our football team began to lose
And Pat Mahomes was hurt and bruised.

Two taped up paws and one bum knee
Left Chiefs fans longing desperately
To see a comeback run ensue
And bring our dream back into view.

And that's exactly what took place
Mahomes returned with guns ablaze.
Each time the Chiefs would get behind
It seemed they simply didn't mind.

They fought and fought and fought some more
Right into Super Bowl fifty-four.
So on a cool Miami night
The Chiefs would face their **biggest** fight.

SUPER BOWL LIV

The Niners from San Francisco
The town that just six years ago
Had stomped on KC's baseball dreams
Now sought to stomp our football team.

Bosa and his band of beasts
Were hungry for a QB feast.
They nipped at Pat Mahomes' toes
Which led to two misguided throws.

San Fran picked the second one
And celebrated like they'd won.
A party must have seemed in order
Ahead by ten in the fourth quarter.

But they forgot the Kingdom's grit.

We fall behind, but never quit.

Third and fifteen, ten points down

With San Fran poised to claim the crown...

Mahomes stepped up and barked the call

That freed the fastest man of all.

The Cheetah hauled a long bomb in

And left defenders sucking wind.

A Kelce score,

 a Watkins catch

A D-Will grab and touchdown stretch.
Before San Fran could check the score
They found themselves now down by four.

Soon the lead grew to eleven.
Chiefs fans thought they'd gone to Heaven.
Frank Clark started to break free
And chase down San Fran's Jimmy G...

Who threw his own misguided toss
Which found a Chief defender's paws.
We could have partied early, too
Just like the Niners chose to do.

But on the sideline Mahomes proclaimed
"We never quit, FINISH THE GAME!"
The San Fran fans all sat in shock
As seconds ticktocked off the clock.

Mahomes dropped back and scrambled right
And fired the ball into the night.
That's when it finally settled in
Chiefs Kingdom had risen once again!

They simply never would give in
And simply willed themselves to win.
You'll face tough odds from time-to-time
You may fall down or fall behind...

But fight just like our boys in red
And never forget what Mahomes said.
When only seconds still remain
True Mahomies "FINISH THE GAME!"

And so, as snow fell gently down
Upon our freshly crowned hometown
We sang and danced around the Lombardi Because...

"YOU GOTTA FIGHT FOR YOUR RIGHT TO PARRRTTTYYYYY!"

Jason Sivewright is the owner of Sweet Boy Books, an LLC based out of Kansas City, Missouri.
Sweet Boy Books creations aim to instill in children a greater sense of identity,
greater self-esteem and the courage to imagine a sweeter world.
When not writing and creating, Jason and his wife Jillian spend their time
with their two young boys (who will someday play for the Royals).

Kevin and Kristen Howdeshell are a husband-and-wife-illustrator duo based
in Kansas City, Missouri. Heading up their studio, The Brave Union,
the team works on posters, packaging, and educational
and editorial illustration with a heavy focus on children's books.
In their non-art-hours, the couple raise their 3 young kids
and are devoted fans of our KC teams!

We (Jason, Kevin and Kristen) would like to dedicate this book to our beloved city.
When we partnered together to write The Night The World Turned Royal Blue
we never could have imagined the wild ride we were in for!

Because of the way KC embraces and supports its local artists we have been able
to meet and share our story with so many. One of the most impactful
visits for us was at Children's Mercy of KC.
Bringing smiles to the faces of those children was an experience we will never forget.

So Kansas City...THANK YOU! On your behalf we are donating
10% of the proceeds of this book to Children's Mercy Hospital of KC.

Let's keep creating and celebrating great stories together.

Made in the USA
Las Vegas, NV
17 December 2024

14137666R00021